The Story of Newgrange

This story was adapted by author Ann Carroll
and illustrated by Derry Dillon

IRELAND'S BEST KNOWN STORIES IN A NUTSHELL

Published 2013
by: In a Nutshell
an imprint of Poolbeg Press Ltd

123 Grange Hill, Baldoyle
Dublin 13, Ireland

Text © Poolbeg Press Ltd 2013

1

ISBN 978 1 84223 598 0

Cover design and illustrations by Derry Dillon
Printed by GPS Colour Graphics Ltd, Alexander Road, Belfast BT6 9HP

This book belongs too

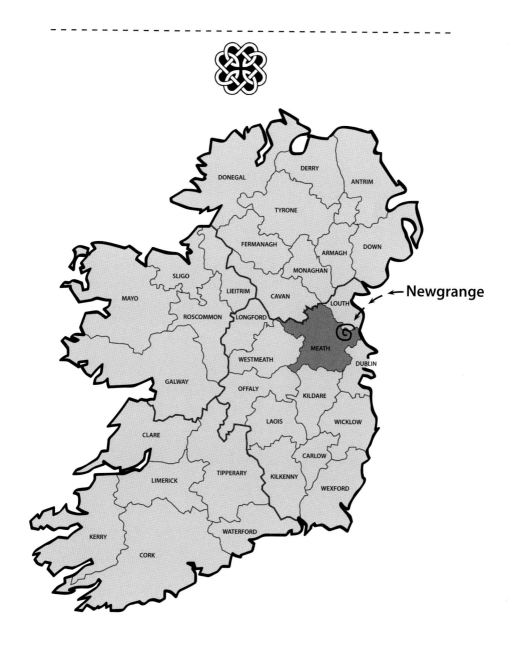

Newgrange

Also in the Nutshell series

5000 Years Ago

All along the Boyne Valley the messengers spread the news. "The new building at Brú na Bóinne is ready!" they told the people. "All the work is finished, and on the shortest day of the year our leaders want you to go there before dawn. Around twenty of you will be chosen to enter the passage leading to the inner chamber and those who are picked will never forget what they see!"

So, on the shortest day, the day of the winter solstice, the crowd gathered well before sunrise. The sky was still starry and the round structure was visible for miles. It rested on a hill, its white stones gleaming.

Magical! they all thought.

In front of the doorway lay a long boulder with fine carvings. A huge flat rock stood beside the entrance, like a door waiting to be closed. Beyond, the passage was black as soot.

Before the stars faded and the sky paled, the chosen number entered, each wondering why there was a large square gap above the doorway. They were not allowed fire-torches and suddenly found themselves in the pitch dark, afraid.

"What are we going to see?" said one, clutching the person in front. "What is it we will never forget?"

"This is like being buried alive," shivered another. "That rock outside could seal the entrance!"

They each held their breath in fright.

Then someone gasped, "No. Look! Look back!"

They turned to see the sun enter the gap over the entrance. A line of light touched the ground and came towards them. And, as it moved, it widened, revealing the carved stonework on each side of the passage. The effect was marvellous.

"The walls and ceiling are golden," they murmured, no longer afraid.

They held up their hands in the shimmering light. "Us too – we're a golden people!"

They watched then as the light travelled down the passage, into the side alcoves. It pointed like a finger at the three spirals carved on the entrance to the end-chamber and glowed on the stone basins there.

They had never seen anything like it. For a long time, as they stood there, the darkness was gone.

It's a sign from the gods, they thought. This is their promise to banish winter so that the longer days of spring will come again.

The Dagda and Aengus Óg

In the years that followed people came to believe the structure we now call Newgrange belonged to The Dagda, the Sun God, for who else could have captured the light at the winter solstice?

The Dagda was a powerful and rich god. He owned the area known as Brú na Bóinne – "The Palace of the Boyne". This included around forty mounds like the one at Newgrange, so he had lots of property.

Now The Dagda had a son, Aengus Óg, and for some unknown reason wanted nothing to do with him. This coldness upset Aengus, especially as he loved Newgrange and wanted to own it.

"Well, you can't have it!" said The Dagda. "It's mine. This is the umpteenth time you've asked. You're most annoying!"

Aengus didn't give up. "Be reasonable. At least let me live there for one day and one night."

"No! Go away!"

But the young god didn't go away and pestered his father until at last The Dagda moaned, "Enough! You're giving me a headache. Newgrange is yours, but only for a day and a night."

"Wonderful! Thank you, Father."

The Dagda grumbled but kept his word and Aengus Óg moved into Newgrange. However, he didn't move out again and when The Dagda found his son still there the next day he was raging.

"Leave at once!" he snarled. "Your time is up!"

"No, it isn't. You said I could stay a day and a night, but you didn't say which day and night. Yesterday could have been the wrong day and night. Today might be right. Then again it might not. I'll have to stay all the time and that way a day and a night sometime or other is bound to be the right day and night."

At this stage The Dagda moaned, head in hands. "I have a migraine listening to you! You're very irritating altogether."

The poor god's brain was addled trying to follow his son's words.

"Keep the place!" he said.

And that's how Aengus Óg came to own Newgrange.

Gods and Humans

Over time the valley of Brú na Bóinne became known as The Other World, because it was where the gods lived. Sometimes their paths crossed with the paths of people from this world. So it happened with the god Aengus Óg and a young man called Diarmuid.

Diarmuid was one of the Fianna, a band of warriors whose chieftain was Fionn Mac Cumhaill. Unfortunately the young man made a terrible enemy of his leader when he fell in love with a beautiful girl called Gráinne who was supposed to marry Fionn, though he was far too old for her. Instead, she eloped with Diarmuid and they married.

Fionn was raging with jealousy and wished to kill the young warrior, but knew he was very popular. So he turned sneaky and pretended to forgive him.

Let him believe we're friends again, Fionn thought. That'll suit my plan!

He invited Diarmuid on a boar-hunt in the forest and made sure the boar was injured just enough to enrage the creature. Diarmuid found himself suddenly alone with the maddened animal and was badly gored.

When Aengus Óg came across him, the young warrior lay dying. The god searched the forest till he found Fionn.

"Diarmuid needs your help!" he said and explained the situation.

"I can do nothing," Fionn told him.

Aengus looked at him. "Everyone knows that water carried from the River Boyne in your hands has the power to heal any wound and any sickness."

Ashamed at being caught out, Fionn went to the river and filled his cupped hands with water. But by the time he reached Diarmuid it had all trickled away. Three times he carried

the water but each time he let it fall through his fingers at the last minute, until finally Diarmuid was dead. And so Fionn got his revenge.

Aengus Óg decided that he at least would
honour the young man and took his body
back to Newgrange. And afterwards it was
said that whenever he wanted company, he'd
bring Diarmuid back to life for a good chat.

Changing Times

It is said too that Newgrange was the burial place of the High Kings until King Cormac Mac Airt refused to be buried there. He was one of the few Christians in Ireland before the time of Saint Patrick.

"Brú na Bóinne is a pagan place," he said. "I'll have none of it and must be laid to rest at Rosnaree." Rosnaree was a village across the river from Newgrange.

Nevertheless, when Cormac died, his followers decided they must bury him with all the other High Kings. But when they attempted to carry his body over the Boyne, the river rose to a great height, ready to crush them. Three times they tried and failed. So Cormac got his wish and was buried at Rosnaree.

After that all the High Kings were buried at Royal Tara, which is not far from Rosnaree.

Years and years passed. The old gods were neglected when Saint Patrick and Christianity came, though they lived on in memory and their stories were still told.

But Newgrange itself was abandoned. By the end of the 17th century much of it had collapsed. Grass covered the sides and roof so that it looked – almost – like any other hill, though people still believed there was something special about it – something to do with the sun and the old gods. Something magical.

The House of the Dead

Over three hundred years ago some workmen who were trying to remove large stones from the odd-looking hill found the entrance to the passage, and Newgrange was rediscovered.

Word spread once more. Many visitors came and much was written. But it wasn't until modern times that the real work began.

In 1962 Professor Michael O'Kelly from

Cork University started to investigate the mound with his team.

As they uncovered and rebuilt Newgrange, the professor wondered about the gap over the entrance. Why would anyone put that over a doorway?

Then he heard local stories about the sun

shining into Newgrange at the winter solstice, which is the 21st of December in our calendar. But no one had actually seen this.

On the shortest day in 1967 the professor

went alone just before dawn and waited in the passage. And so he was the first person since ancient times to see the darkness turn to gold for seventeen minutes.

It took thirteen years for the professor and

his team to bring Newgrange back to the way
it had looked 5000 years ago.

Many questions were asked:

How did the first builders manage to lift those great stones?

Why were Roman coins left there? Who owned them – and the pottery pieces, pendants and flint objects – all from different ages?

Why do so many stories connect the gods with Newgrange? Was it built for them?

The bones of five humans were found there. Was it a burial place?

No one has the answer for sure to any of these questions.

Professor O'Kelly said he thought Newgrange

might have been built not as a grave but as a House of the Dead, where the spirits of special people would live for a long time.

Nowadays so many people want to visit Newgrange at the solstice that there is a national draw each year for places. But visitors are welcome at any season and on every tour there is a re-enactment of that golden light entering the passage – this time at the flick of a switch.

Whatever its past, Newgrange is a place of great mystery. Perhaps that's why it's so haunting. It is easy to believe that spirits still live there.

The End

Word Sounds

(Opinions may differ regarding pronunciation)

Words	Sounds
Aengus	Eyn-gus
Bóinne	Bo-in-neh
Brú	Broo
Cumhaill	Cool
Dagda	Dag-da
Diarmuid	Deer-mid
Fianna	Fee-ana
Fionn	Fee-un
Mac	Mock
Óg	Oh-g (hard g)

Also available from the IN A NUTSHELL series

All you need to know about Ireland's best loved stories in a nutshell

The Salmon of Knowledge

Available Now!

The Story of Saint Patrick

Available Now!

How Cúchulainn Got His Name

Available Now!

The Children of Lir

Available Now!

POOLBEG WISHES TO
THANK YOU
for buying a Poolbeg book.

If you enjoyed this why not
visit our website:

www.poolbeg.com

and get another book delivered straight to
your home or to a friend's home!

All books despatched within 24 hours.

POOLBEG

WHY NOT JOIN OUR MAILING LIST
@ www.poolbeg.com and get some
fantastic offers on Poolbeg books